IMAGES
of England

Peak District
Mining and Quarrying

Nicking (i.e. taking the title to) Bacon Close Mine at Youlgreave, probably in the 1920s. Barmaster Alfred Hodgkiss, who lived at Baslow, has his hand on the stows. (PD)

NAMHO

The National Association of Mining History Organisations was founded in 1979. It is a registered charity (No.297301) that promotes the interests of those seeking to preserve the relics and history of our mining past. The association currently represents over sixty member organisations and acts as a national pressure group and a focus for liaison between members. It encourages the improvement of research techniques and devises guidelines and codes of practice. A mining history conference is held every two years.

For more details of local mining history societies or to obtain copies of NAMHO's codes of practice, please contact: The Secretary, NAMHO, c/o Peak District Mining Museum, Matlock Bath, Derbyshire, DE4 3NJ.

NAMHO wishes to emphasise that old mines are potentially dangerous and should not be explored underground without an experienced guide. Permission should always be obtained before venturing onto private property and the mention of a particular site does not imply any right of access.

IMAGES
of England

Peak District
Mining and Quarrying

Lynn Willies and Harry Parker

in conjunction with the
National Association of Mining History Organisations
and the Peak District Mining Museum

TEMPUS

Outside the dressing coe at Golconda Mine, Brassington, *c.*1907. (HMP)

First published 2004
Reprinted 2000, 2004, 2006

Tempus Publishing Limited
The Mill, Brimscombe Port,
Stroud, Gloucestershire, GL5 2QG
www.tempus-publishing.com

British Library Cataloguing in Publication Data.
A catalogue record for this book is available from the British Library.

ISBN-10: 0 7524 1710 X
ISBN-13: 978 0 7524 1710 3

Typesetting and origination by Tempus Publishing Limited.
Printed in Great Britain.

Contents

A reconstruction of a working stows at the Peak District Mining Museum, showing the Wills Founder engine in the background. (HMP)

Introduction

Open moors with rocky edges, deep valleys, some dry, others with rushing streams, ancient trackways and footpaths, hamlets, villages and small towns – the Peak District nowadays is often looked on as a 'playground' for walkers, climbers, underground explorers and those who come simply to appreciate its beauties. But this was also one of England's most important industrial areas, in which those working in mining and quarrying, as well as in woollen manufacture and later the early cotton industry, still had close, often direct, links with agriculture. Today, mining has not quite vanished, but only occupies a few dozen people, quarrying is still substantial but output is concentrated in relatively few quarries which are highly mechanised employing some hundreds of people, while the eighteenth-century usurper, cotton manufacture, has also all but vanished. Agriculture is suffering terribly, with considerable areas of land neglected, and vistas free of trees since Bronze and Iron Age times are being overrun with scrub. Once almost self-contained villages are now occupied by commuters. In this book we try to give a glimpse of the area's past mining and quarrying industry, the people who worked in it and its importance, not just to the Peak, but to the people and places elsewhere which were served by it. Finally, we have included a short section on the legacy that has been left us and how it is being dealt with.

The boundaries of the true Peak District are hard to define. The modern-day National Park is a political division, which extends west of Derbyshire into Staffordshire and Cheshire and northwards to Yorkshire. Because of higher populations and industrial use, some western, and wide areas of the eastern, parts of the area were omitted from the National Park. For present purposes the boundaries extend over all of the Carboniferous Limestone and Millstone Grit of the National Park and adjacent areas. A case could be made to include parts of the Coal Measures too, but industrially these are better treated as a separate unit.

The geological terms Carboniferous Limestone and Millstone Grit are really time units and include a broad range of rocks and minerals. The former includes a variety of limestones but also igneous rocks such as basaltic lavas, doleritic intrusions and volcanic ash or tuff ejected from volcanoes, while the Millstone Grit is made up of thick layers of shales and sandstone which vary considerably in their character. Both include minerals important for economic products:

Ores of lead, copper, zinc, iron, manganese and magnesium.
Bulk limestone aggregates, building stones, tufa and ornamental limestones or 'marbles'.
Chert (a hard siliceous rock).
Hard volcanic and igneous stones for road-toppings.
Industrial (formerly gangue or waste) minerals – fluorspar (including the 'Blue John' ornamental variety), barite, calcite and oxides of iron (limonite, haematite and ochre) and manganese (black wad).

> Sandstones such as the coarse gritstone, building stones and finer grained whetstones and refractory (or fire-) stones.
> Clays for brick and cement working.
> Refractory sands and clays for brick making.

Coal also occurs in the Millstone Grit rocks (for instance, above Chatsworth House and at Axe Edge above Buxton) but is not further followed here. There are also minor occurrences of bitumen, oil and small amounts of 'china clay' which have been worked as curiosities. Of course, if extracted from underground, it is also possible to include water as a mineral deposit – in which case it would be in the billion-ton-plus class!

Today, besides water, the major outputs are of limestone, for aggregate and chemical use, gritstone, for building, and fluorspar for use as a flux in the metal industries and as a chemical feedstock (especially for plastics). Barite, which was first used as a lead substitute in paints such as lithopone (barite and zinc oxide) around 1850, is today important as a filler for papers and paints and for drilling mud. Calcite is used in decorative floors such as terrazzo and external finishes such as spar-dash as well as for infilling between curbs in graveyards, etc. A little lead ore (galena or lead sulphide) is produced as a by-product of fluorspar and barite exploitation and is smelted to produce the metal. It has also been used in small quantities in brake linings, a local manufacture. Iron oxides, found commonly in mineral veins, used to be used for iron smelting or for colour in the substantial number of small paint works in the district, though nowadays these works rely on imports. Manganese oxide, known as black wad, was also tried for paint making but this was soon given up due to the tendency for spontaneous combustion, but small amounts were used in the Sheffield steel industry which developed the hard-wearing manganese steels. Zinc ores, known locally by the pejorative name blackjack, began to assume greater importance as galvanising expanded from the late nineteenth century onwards. The local zinc industry was important enough for a smelter – a spelter works – to be built alongside the canal at Hartshay near Ripley.

Before the late eighteenth century, it was lead alone for which the Peak was famous. It has mostly been found in the Carboniferous Limestone rocks together with fluorspar, barite and calcite, which were then looked on only as waste. However, its smelting spread the lead industry into the wooded valleys of the Millstone Grit rocks and the Coal Measures where there was abundant water power and wood and, later, coal for fuel. During the eighteenth century earlier small workings for copper at Ecton were deepened and flourished for the best part of that century – much of the profit went into the Duke of Devonshire's development of Buxton.

Both lead and copper had a very old history, now known to have commenced some 3,500 years ago in the Bronze Age. Lead was a major product in Romano-British times, but thereafter declined until the late medieval period, in the twelfth century onwards. The purity of the lead was so good that it was particularly suitable for sheet lead and thus roofed a substantial number of churches, monasteries and castles. Its peak period came about almost accidentally. The destruction of the monasteries under Henry VIII resulted in an enormous surplus of lead which destroyed the European industry. As it recovered, towards the last years of the sixteenth century, new production and smelting methods led to Derbyshire becoming the leading producer, with its products being exported all over the world for the next two centuries, often by the Dutch and English East India Companies.

By the eighteenth century this supremacy was lost as other areas, in the mid- and north Pennines and in Wales, began to develop new and richer fields. At the end of that century lead also began to come in from Spain. In the nineteenth century the industry, despite modest revivals, was in decline, its end, but for one major exception, coming with cheaper imports still from Australia and the United States. The exception was Millclose Mine, restarted in 1859, becoming a major producer some ten years later and, after a considerable and desperately important last find in 1929, so becoming Britain's greatest ever lead mine. Ten years later it was closed, though its associated lead smelter is still in production today, recycling lead batteries.

Miners at Lees Shaft, Millclose Mine, 1936. (LW)

Lead mining had a major impact on nearly all aspects of life in the area. Around 1643 some 20,000 people in the Peak, including families, were dependent on the lead business – at that time a population equivalent to one of the largest cities. However, most miners lived in villages whose population ebbed and flowed with the prosperity of local mines. Winster, for example, probably grew from three or four hundred people in the late seventeenth century to about 2,000 within the next sixty or so years. Villages such as Castleton, Bradwell, Hucklow, Eyam, Calver, Youlgreave (or Auld Grove = old mine), Elton, Bonsall and Brassington and the town of Wirksworth, like Winster, were dominated by the industry and grew much larger than would have been possible with agriculture alone.

Despite this, miners were not necessarily in the majority. Farming was still important and mining families often combined their trade with a small farm, hence the many tiny fields seen in the mining villages to occupy their 'two beasts, stirk and a pig'. Miners needed tools and it was not unusual to have several village blacksmiths and whitesmiths as well as carpenters, ropemakers, candlemakers, builders and so on producing for both mining and domestic purposes. There were shops aplenty and alehouses and pubs – twenty-four in Winster – to serve the miners on pay nights. Wives and children were often employed in washing the ore at the mine, but many villages also had a domestic woollen cloth industry and, after Arkwright's successful demonstration of cotton manufacture, many left to work at one of the new mills. Horses were needed, to work the engines on deep shafts, to convey the ore to the smelting mills, by 'jagging' (carrying packs) or in two-wheeled carts, and to bring in the wood, water and coal needed at the mines. Smelting required many fewer workers, but the mills needed fuel, wood (dried wood was known as white coal) or, later, coal which again needed getters and carriers. From the mills, lead was carted to heads of navigation at Derby, Chesterfield, the River Idle near Bawtry and Tinsley near Sheffield, most of it going on to Hull and then, via London and Amsterdam, to its markets around the world.

Mining and smelting needed a middle and upper class too. There were mine agents who managed the mines, of both modest means and greater, engine builders, surveyors, a surprising number of lawyers and attorneys (for mining men were notoriously litigious), merchants in both ore and metal, mine owners and substantial shareholders who took a direct interest in their holdings. There were also the royalty owners and lessees – notably the Dukes of Devonshire and Rutland, but some lesser men too who owned or farmed the mineral rights from the Duchy of Lancaster, the Crown. The wealthiest occupied the many substantial houses seen in the Peak, nearly all of whose founding families had at least part of their wealth based on lead.

The decline of lead mining after about 1780 often resulted in much misery. By 1798 Winster, its mining boom over, was described as much decayed, with its population down to half that of

Iminent collapse necessitated emergency repairs on Magpie Mine in January 1974. Chestnut palings were erected around the dangerous brickwork and the chimney's interior was stuffed with straw. This was the first restoration work on Magpie. (HMP)

A view from the chimney during the repairs shows the mine's powder-house and engine reservoir covered in snow. The line of Butts Vein is shown by the hillocks stretching into the distance. (HMP)

forty years earlier and a high level of poverty. Many of the poor were no doubt still there because of age or because they had sufficient land to eke out an existence. Others, however, had clearly moved on. Some went to other mining areas such as Yorkshire, Wales and the north Pennines where there had always been close family connections and migrations. Substantial numbers went into quarrying – of gritstone and limestone – which, though always part of the local economy, was rapidly becoming a major industry. This was especially the result of transport developments such as the Cromford Canal and the Peak Forest Canal at Whaley Bridge. These were eventually both linked by the Cromford and High Peak Railway in 1830 which, with later railway development, opened up the area for the supply of bulk products to the outside world. Many other residents, despite a reluctance to abandon the 'adventure' of lead mining for a supposedly inferior occupation, fled into coal mining, an industry which virtually surrounded the Peak. Other men as well as very many more women were able to find employment in the cotton mills and associated industries set up by Arkwright and his imitators.

Later, in the middle years of the nineteenth century, with a short-lived revival of lead mining, a considerable number of Cornish miners were employed – skilled men brought in to introduce new methods. A few stayed but decline caused them and native Derbyshire miners to search again for work elsewhere. Some, like lead smelter owner John Alsop, left for Australia (in his case leaving his debts behind him) and others no doubt took part in the gold rushes in the United States and Australia after 1849. After Millclose Mine closed in 1939 several skilled men are known to have gone mining in Australia and South Africa whilst others facing unemployment were 'saved' by the war.

In a few places tourism had begun even before the decline. Matlock Bath, whose few miners' hovels were compared to pigsties by Defoe around 1725, was given that name some decades after its first bath opened in 1697-1698. Former miners could earn the equivalent of a day's pay for taking the more adventurous or credulous visitor down one or other local mines and could find a ready market for minerals and other petrifactions. Castleton was equally busy with visitors and many other mining villages were able to modestly supplement their income in this way.

The new industries – quarrying, coal, and cotton – sometimes required their own settlement development, though a number, including Castleton, Bradwell, Tideswell, Calver, Matlock, Bonsall and Wirksworth, for example, were close enough to both quarries and cotton mills to maintain their size and even grow, perhaps especially Wirksworth which had several of each. Among specialised quarrying villages perhaps the most important were in the west of the area, at Bugsworth (now Buxworth) and near Chapel-en-le-Frith and Buxton. Within the coal mining areas of the Peak, the numbers employed at the invariably small mines were low and it was the deeper mines further east that developed in the railway age which needed the rapid growth and model villages of what we now think of as the coalfield area.

The extractive industries have left us a huge legacy. There are an estimated 25,000 lead mining shafts for instance and substantial areas have waste heaps which contain varying amounts of toxic minerals, notably lead. Some lead mining and stone quarrying areas have recently been restored as 'derelict land'. Such land is often of low grade and, ironically, sometimes of less landscape variety and quality than had it been left untreated. Much of the affected but untreated areas are of very substantial botanical, mineral and scenic interest, capable of supporting a wide range of often rare species (such as orchids and metallophytes like leadwort and the wild pansy) and providing leisure and educational facilities. To the astonishment of mining and quarrying companies, opposition to development has not always come from opponents of noise, pollution and traffic (though a hidden agenda might sometimes be suspected) but stems from the damage renewed activity would cause to specialised plant communities, mature woodland, mineral exposures and heritage sites, all the result of previous mining and quarrying activity.

One less welcome legacy is the high level of lead to be found on some sites: average soil levels are some ten times as high as in non-mining and -smelting areas, with very much higher levels still on many mining and smelting sites. This creates few problems in practice, but it is a good idea for safety reasons not to let children play on old heaps and to ensure that hands are washed before eating.

Should you wish to learn more and visit the many sites which are easy to access, the obvious starting point is the Peak District Mining Museum at Matlock Bath (adjacent to the A6 road and open all year – Tel. 01629 583834). This has a small mine attached to it and other mines, especially the Masson Cavern and Great Rutland Cavern, can be visited on the Heights of Abraham, with many interesting sites and views on the hillside beyond the public areas. Access to the spectacular mines on High Tor is free. At Castleton the Treak Cliff and Blue John Caves were both mines and the Speedwell Mine was a drainage sough. A walk up the disused road from Speedwell to Blue John will lead past the Odin Mine. Numerous other sites (and guidebooks) can be located at the Museum, but Magpie Mine, near the village of Sheldon is the best known and access is free. Almost any walk on the limestone hills on the west side of the Derwent Valley will lead to mining remains. Of mining villages the best preserved is undoubtedly Winster, about five miles from Matlock, but again, almost any village in the mining area still displays its links for those who search.

The best guide to the area is the forthcoming edition of *Lead Mining in the Peak District* by T.D. Ford and J.H. Rieuwerts, which is available from the Peak District Mining Museum and all good bookshops.

When exploring the mines, there is a code of practice we ask you to follow:

> Respect the countryside and recognise that it is the farmers' home and workplace.
> Keep to the highways and public footpaths.
> Do not enter hollows or remove shaft covers and beware of open shafts which may well have dangerous sides about to collapse.
> Keep children and pets under very close control.
> Beware falling stones on old buildings.
> Do not damage walls or remove vegetation.
> Do not enter a mine without a capable guide.
> Wash hands before eating after being on a lead site.
> Join a caving club or a special outdoor pursuits course if you do wish to go underground other than in a show mine (ask at the Peak District Mining Museum for suitable guidance on this).
> If a member of your party gets into trouble in a mine, the Derbyshire Cave Rescue is alerted by dialling the police on 999 and asking for Cave Rescue.

Unlike a pictorial record of a relatively modern industry, the availability of contemporaneous photographs of mining and quarrying is not adequate to give a reasonably complete story. Instead we have chosen to employ a mix of original contemporary sources including sketches, paintings and even rhyme, with, of course, photographs for the later working period, together with photographs of artefacts and remains taken since work stopped. Some of these latter photographs are themselves almost a century old, illustrating that even then there was a growing consciousness that times were changing and old ways were disappearing, but others are recent or relatively recent. Though few sought to record underground working when much of it was carried out, it is the good fortune of mining historians and archaeologists that, underground, left undisturbed, things can remain the same for centuries. Both the present authors have been involved for several decades in recording mining and quarrying and to a considerable degree this is a record of the work of themselves and their colleagues as much as the people and sites remembered by it.

One
Early Mining

Very little is known of mining until after medieval times. The earliest artefacts found in or on mines are tools such as hammer-stones and an antler tool, recently discovered at the Ecton copper mines in Staffordshire. The antler tool has now been radiocarbon-dated to the Bronze Age. A ceremonial lead axe from Mam Tor near Castleton of the same period is probably the oldest known product of the lead mines nearby.

There are also traces of enhanced lead levels in peats of this same age found on Kinderscout, which may relate to smelting activity, either in the immediate area or wider afield. Later periods – the Iron Age and the Romano-British era – all show up as much greater peaks, with the highest in the Industrial Age of the eighteenth and nineteenth centuries. It is much diminished today.

Substantial evidence of smelting, but not the associated mining, comes from finds of Romano-British age. On land over thirty Roman ingots have been found which derived from Derbyshire and a recent wreck site near Cherbourg has found many more – some marked 'ICENI', the name of the tribe who lived east of the Trent. Such survivals indicate widespread activity, as does the presence of a fort and civil settlement at the north end of the mining field – Navio, near Bradwell – and a major civil settlement at what is now the Carsington Reservoir, probably the Lutudarum whose name appears on several ingots. These two sites are connected by an even older road, later called the Portway, which was improved in Roman times. The few Roman smelting sites so far found are all off the mining field, two east of Chesterfield and another near Duffield.

Medieval mining is almost equally unrepresented. Lead works, which may mean mines or smelters, were mentioned in the Domesday Survey, and there is documentary evidence of mining at Nestus, now part of the show mine system on the Heights of Abraham at Matlock Bath, in the fourteenth century. There are also a score or more of Bole Hills in the area with abundant slag remains, where lead was smelted until a new process came in around 1580. This was a 'bonfire technology', with large wood fires relying on the high winds along the gritstone edges to attain a sufficiently high temperature. Two major items from this period are available: the earliest written laws of lead mining from the Ashbourne Inquisition of 1288 and the carving of a medieval miner in Wirksworth Church, which is probably even older.

The Ecton antler tool is around 3750 years old. It was found in the upper workings of the mine. (Graham Bunting)

A Romano-British lead smelting hearth from near Duffield. It was built over an earlier group of pottery kilns and probably belongs to the fourth or fifth century AD. It is now in the Peak District Mining Museum. (HMP)

Romano-British lead ingots from the wreck at Ploumenách, near Cherbourg, Normandy. These probably also belong to the fourth or fifth century and most likely have a Peak District origin. The rounded forms may originate from a hearth such as that shown previously.

There are a wide range of markings, some including the inscription 'ICENI', the British tribe who lived in East Anglia, possibly with a territory ranging as far west as the Trent. (LW)

Many of the ingots found on land are more regular in form, like this one of two found near Ashbourne. This may mean, of course, that lead ingots not obviously of the Roman period were recycled by their finders! The inscription means 'From the works of Lutudarum' and 'From Britain / without silver'. (LW)

This carving, removed from Bonsall Church to Wirksworth Church in the nineteenth century, shows a medieval miner. Comparison with continental forms of carving suggests it predates the twelfth century. (PD)

Two

Mining Law

In medieval times the Peak was part waste and hunting forest, part a mining area owned by the Crown or its vassals. A royalty on all ore mined of a thirteenth, known as 'lot', went to the Crown (in its right as the Duchy of Lancaster) and a tithe, or tenth, was paid to the Church. So as to encourage mining, it was made a 'free' mining area with wide and unusual privileges. The 'free miners' were encouraged to work by very liberal laws which are still largely in force, permitting search for lead ore in the 'liberties' anywhere but in churchyards, gardens, orchards and highways. The miners had rights of access, water and space to both mine and dump their waste without regard to the land users' or owners' wishes.

To control mining in what may well be compared to the Wild West of America, mineral courts were set up with a Steward and Barmaster representing the Duchy and a Grand Jury of twenty four men (twelve since 1851-1852) appointed for six months to control each of the different areas. The laws represented common and practical experience and could develop from decisions made by the jurors. These were not fully listed until the mid-seventeenth century when Thomas Manlove, a Barmoot Steward, wrote them down 'in metre'. His original manuscript still exists and is displayed in the Peak District Mining Museum. It was said that miners' children learned the rules in Manlove's poem 'at their mother's pap'.

The mining laws were codified in 1851-1852 and though some of the more peculiar items were omitted the fundamentals were maintained. The Court still sits regularly today, made up of men who have a wide knowledge of the miners and mining field.

The Barmoot Court at Wirksworth. Built in 1815, it is known to be the third such building in Wirksworth. Other areas used a local public house. The jury is nowadays appointed annually in early April in a ceremony at the court. (HMP)

For ftealing oar twice from the Minery,
The Thief that's taken fined twice fhall be,
But the third time that he commits fuch theft,
Shall have a Knife ftruck through his hand to th'haft,
Into the Stow, and there till death fhall ftand ,
Or loofe himfelf by Cutting loofe his hand;
And fhall forfwear the franchife of the Mine,
And always lofe his freedom from that time.

Part of Manlove's poem. The penalty for theft was harsh, bearing comparison with similar penalties in the Wild West of later years.

The court in 1979. Shown are, from left to right, back: deputy Barmaster John Mort (Junior), jurors Roger Bacon, Jack Eidson, Albert Rockarch, Philip Dagger, Philip Gregory, Rupert Bishop. Front: foreman Harold Buckley, Jack Beck, Lawrence Musson, J.H. Rieuwerts, Lionel Gregory, Eric Fisher, steward Michael Brooke Taylor. (HMP)

The bronze standard dish. Wooden copies were standardized by filling with rape seed and either gouging with a chisel to make the wooden dish larger or planing the top to reduce its size. (LW)

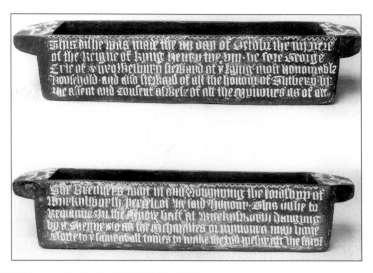

The main duty of the Barmaster was to measure the ore and ensure proper title to mines. Here in 1908 at Northcliffe Sough Lead and Fluorspar Mine, Calver, he prepares to measure some twelve tons of ore. Masters and men form a fine contrast though both probably carefully chose their clothes for the photograph. (HMP)

SOKE
and WAPENTAKE of
WIRKSWORTH

NOTICE IS HEREBY GIVEN,
that if this Mine called *Gorseydale*
in the Liberty of *Bonsall*
is not put into proper workmanship by the
rightful owner, within three weeks from
this date, it will be given away without
further Notice.

Wm Erskine

BARMASTER.

Dated this *28th* day of *March* 19 *88*

Brooks Press, Wirksworth.

A 'nicking notice'. Until the laws were modified in 1851-1852, an unworked mine could be claimed. This meant a visit by the Barmaster for each of three weeks when he placed a nick with a knife on the barrel of the windlass to warn the owner of impending forfeit. This was sometimes done with some stealth, which was frowned on – thus the likely modern use of 'nicking' as 'not-quite-stealing'. Nowadays a notice is pinned at the mine and at the local post office. (HMP)

The nicking process was often, and is sometimes still, used to confirm ownership of a mine title. The first dish of ore has to be paid over as the freeing dish or 'entry fine', which confers title. Here, in 1988, the seventh centenary of our knowledge of the laws, Gorsey Dale Mine on Bonsall Moor has its first dish of ore weighed by the Barmaster. Present are, from left to right: Philip Gregory, Barmaster William Erskine, owner Lionel Gregory and juryman Tony Wragg. (HMP)

Three

Lead Mines and Miners

Before photography neither mines nor miners were common subjects for artistic expression. Though a few illustrations are available and maps sometimes have crude figures drawn on them, we mainly know of both men and their work from documentary sources, from inscriptions and from the archaeological remains which can be found in many hundreds of accessible mines. Nowadays the remains of mining are very widespread with thousands of mine hillocks and open or capped shafts. Though sites have often been disturbed by recent mining, large areas remain as they were left a century and a half ago or longer.

The symbol of a mine at work was the stows, or windlass, mounted on the shafts both at the surface and underground. Mines were owned by their length in 'meers' of 29-31yds, depending on the liberty and local mining laws. Originally one or two meers was enough for a small mine and each had a shaft to allow ventilation of the workings. Each meer had to have a stows on its shaft to show it was in ownership. As mines became bigger, the unused shafts had stakes to mark the meers, each with a small model stows – a 'posen', or possession, stows – nailed to it. These stakes ran across the countryside marking the position of veins below. The habit of Victorian tourists of removing the model stows as souvenirs put the ownership of the mines at risk, and the practice was abandoned in 1851-1852. This destroyed a small source of income for old men who made the model stows and walked the 'possessions' to see they were in order.

Larger and deeper mines, even as late as the late nineteenth century, commonly used a horse gin (engine), for winding. This was almost as often for winding water as it was for waste or ore. One-horse gins were the most common, but some gins needed as many as four horses. At Watergrove Mine near Wardlow the horses used were often those blinded in accidents, an economy possible because of the simple circular path the horse had to follow. This must have had especial appeal to the mine agent, William Wyatt, who felt an agent's duty was to 'save every sixpence'. All his mines lost large sums of money over a period of some forty years in the middle of the nineteenth century.

Although shafts are the easiest way to access mines, many entries are horizontal or sometimes inclined. Drainage tunnels were called 'soughs' and were driven from a nearby valley. These can be very small and short, but a number were substantial and enormously expensive ventures, running for distances of up to three miles and taking up to thirty years to complete. The earliest known were driven in the mid-sixteenth century but the region's great soughs were driven particularly in the middle years of the eighteenth, though the last, the $1\frac{1}{4}$-mile-long Magpie Sough, was not driven until 1873-1884.

Left: George G. Blackwell of Grindleford was owner of the Northcliffe Sough Lead and Fluorspar Mine at Calver. He is shown here around 1908 with his *L'ordre de Sauveur* medal. (PDMM)
Right: Thomas Hampson Brown of Bakewell, who died in 1916 aged sixty-three, was an auctioneer, accountant and also manager of Magpie Mine at Sheldon and Gank Hole in Lathkill Dale. (HMP)

A share certificate for the Magpie Mine in 1877, signed by John Fairburn, the main shareholder and manager, and other directors. The financial collapse of the mine in 1885 left him, in his own words, a 'ruined man'. He died six months later. In earlier years a note of the ownership of shares in the Barmaster's books was sufficient and usually the only title. (LW)

This drawing was produced in 1823 to show the location of the supposed bones of a rhinoceros in Dream Mine, Wirksworth. It is the sole picture available of a small but complete mine. At the surface there is the thatched 'coe', for storage of tools and ore, and the usual stows for winding. Two shafts provide ventilation, winding and access, with the second shaft being plumbed, possibly to add artistic balance to the picture. Below is a fairly typical pipe working with alluvial debris being simply picked and shovelled and then raised to the surface for separation. (LW)

Mine hillocks near Ryder Point on Middleton Moor. (HMP)

John Lawson on Brassington Moor, c.1960, with the last pair of working stows left on the mining field. (HMP)

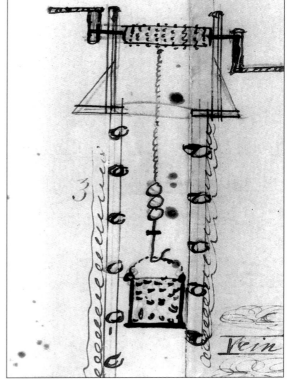

A drawing of a winding and climbing shaft, mid-nineteenth century, from the Rieuwerts Collection. Note the footholds in the sides and what appears to be chain holding the fire-bucket to assist with the ventilation of the mine. Despite, or perhaps because of, the obvious danger of climbing in such shafts, to depths of sometimes over 300ft, there were very few accidents. Later nineteenth-century mechanised methods were much more dangerous. (DRO)

Deep mines were descended in stages, often 60 to 100 feet or so each. Here is a stows in Stadford Hollow Mine, on Longstone Edge near Monsall Head, at the top of an internal shaft or sump. The lad (labourer) who wound it stood unprotected on a tiny platform in a dog-leg in the shaft, transferring the load on to the 'clieve', or hook, of a rope coming down to him from the surface. (LW)

Below, the wrought-iron bucket sat awaiting filling for some 150 years. (LW)

A horse gin at Godbehere (pronounced Godber) Founder on Cromford Moor, near Black Rocks, c.1815. The shaft below it is shown to have collapsed. This happened in 1797 and John Boden and Anthony Pearson were entombed near the shaft bottom under 54yds of earth and rocks. Three days later Pearson was found dead, but Boden was found after eight days, emaciated but alive, and was back at work fourteen weeks later. He had tried to eat his tallow candles but found them too revolting. Boden was winding from a station in the shaft and Pearson was hanging-on at the bottom. (from Mawe's *Mineralogy*, 1825. LW)

The last surviving, but long-disused, horse gin at Snake Mine, Middleton Moor, c.1920. The photograph was taken by F.H. Brindley. The horse was attached on the right while a 'trail' suspended from the left side of the arm prevented inadvertent reversing during winding. (PD)

The huge shaft at Hardrake Mine, Sheldon. Sunk around 1840 using a horse gin, it is about 240ft deep and was so large as to allow proposed later use of a steam engine. The mine was one of William Wyatt's expensive failures. Following a search for a murder weapon a few years ago, it has now been covered. (RB)

Shafts were often divided by timber brattices both to form winding and climbing compartments and to assist ventilation. This is an underground shaft at Wills Founder Mine at Winster from which the water had been pumped to allow exploration. Rusting of the iron nails has caused the vertical boards to fall off, exposing the climbing-way stemples. Immersion in water and perhaps the presence of lead and zinc meant the wood, 150 years later, was still in good condition. (LW)

Wooden and iron ladders in Ecton Copper Mine from Salts Level down to Deep Ecton, Staffordshire, with Mike Luff and daughter Margaret. These belong to the twentieth century, but their condition is not unusual; preservation in copper mines is often very good. (HMP)

Miners abandoned these tools in Old Jant, or Gentlewoman's, Mine probably in around 1855. Archaeological evidence suggests they had been clearing a fall in a shaft which fell in again, possibly proving enough discouragement to cause abandonment. The tools here include drilling and tamping tools for use with black powder, a pick and a riddle. (PD)

Few personal artefacts survive. This small clog was found probably in the 1920s and was thought rare enough to be photographed. Recent discoveries in one mine suggest the miners changed their clay-encrusted footwear before climbing the ladders out of the mine. (LW)

Personal details of miners are rare. This graffiti showing a figure in tall hat, high-heeled shoes and frock coat was found in Gentlewoman's Pipe and is probably late seventeenth- or early eighteenth-century in date. It was nicknamed the 'overseer' by its discoverers on the grounds that the clothing was not suitable for working underground. (LW)

Earlier soughs were small in section and some, where they were driven through hard limestone rock before black powder or gunpowder were in common use, relied on pick-and-wedge methods of excavation. To do this, a groove about two inches (50mm) deep was picked in the face or forefield from roof to sole, and another made about two inches from it. The intervening rock was then broken away using a wedge. In a shift of six hours about two inches of driving was done. The passage was made to fit an average miner, giving a coffin-like section. Here, in Fountrabby Sough near Cromford, lack of maintenance means the floor has filled in and movement is as uncomfortable as it appears. (RB – scale and photograph)

An abandoned forefield, this one from the 1740s in Masson Sough in Matlock, showing pick marks and the initials nearby of a miner. Near this place, a small chamber reveals that the miners or the agent were uncertain which way to go, starting several small headings and then abandoning them. If one shift a day was worked, then it took some three months to make up their minds! (PD)

The driving of Meerbrook Sough, driven from the River Derwent near Whatstandwell, began in 1777, inspired by Francis Hurt. One branch went to Black Rocks (to the Godbehere and other mines) the other to the town and mines of Wirksworth. To ventilate the mine, a shaft sunk from the top of the Wirksworth Moor used boring rods to locate it below, but failed to do so. A cat was then taken in to see if it could indicate the position of the rods and whether by this means or not they eventually holed through. Today this mine is used as a source of water and is truly a water mine with a production of some 12-15 million gallons per day. (HMP – the figure is Lynn Willies)

Inside, the Meerbrook Sough is arched as it passes through soft and unstable shale. Here it divides and there has been partial collapse. Maintenance has been neglected now for over a century and some concern has been expressed about the possible consequences if ever a major collapse takes place and the water seeks its former outlets. (PD)

The entrance to Magpie Sough (driven between 1873 and 1884) in around 1900, showing a boat used for transporting zinc ore and calcite down the sough. The boat was taken across the River Wye and unloaded into carts. (Derbyshire Pennine Club Collection, HMP)

The newly constructed Magpie Sough boat is tried out near the weir below the sough tail. (HMP)

The gradient of Magpie Sough was about twelve feet in the mile, enough – with the swift flow this produced – to keep the floor free of silt. However, for boat use it was necessary to install flash locks. Moving upstream, these ponded the water allowing easy passage. Chains hung from the roof were used to pull the boat in. Full boats 'flashed' downstream when the single sets of gates were opened, thus providing relatively efficient passage. (RB – the figure is Peter Challis)

Most water enters Magpie Sough about a mile in. Beyond that a railway was installed to connect with the actual mine. Note the 'grip' to channel the water and the passage's regular shape from the use of drills and gelignite blasting. Peter Challis acts as a scale. It is easier to push a waggon in and out than to try and walk upright unencumbered due to the effects of both the water and the low roof. (RB)

Graffiti in the form of initials and dates are fairly common, especially near shaft bottoms where the job of 'hanger on' must have been very tedious. This example is from Masson Cavern at Matlock Bath, made high on the wall before the alluvial debris was removed. It probably represents a team of 'copers' (miners working in co-partnership) who had taken a bargain to work in the mine. (LW)

'J Taylor aged 12 years' is an unusually emotive and informative scratching, made on the muddy underside of a ledge by smoking with a candle and scratching with a nail or similar tool. At that age he would have had a fairly simple task – moving ore from workplace to shaft, perhaps. (PD)

34

Four
The Deposits and their Working

Little has so far been said of the mineral deposits and the actual workings – called 'stopes' – within them that the shafts and soughs were made to reach. This reflects what is often reality today: the accesses are open, but the mineral areas have either been very small, blocked off by falls or filled with waste rock. However, the deposits take three main forms.

Most spectacular at surface is the rake, a mineral-filled fault from a few feet to many feet wide and sometimes miles long. These have often been worked from surface, sometimes recently reworked. Horizontal grooves and corrugations on the walls indicate the direction of the rock's movement in the geological phenomenon known as a 'wrench fault'. Underground, the worked-out rake was usually filled with waste mineral supported on timber or stone stemples above passages, but in some cases they have been almost completely emptied, allowing the full form to be seen.

Narrow veins, the second type, are often infilled joints that frequently contain valuable lead ore to an even greater extent than the rakes. These were called 'scrins' by the miners. They can result in very narrow workings indeed as the miners as far as possible avoided removal of anything but ore.

Finally, the richest deposits were often in pipes – old caves or solutional cavities that became lined and infilled by layers of mineral. Sometimes, natural weathering from water passing through loosened the mineral, which was then sorted by the flow into heavier (i.e. lead ore) and lighter (waste) portions, resulting in very rich finds indeed, needing little but pick and shovel to work them out.

Geologists get much information about mineral deposits from old maps. These were very rare before the mid- and late eighteenth century, the miners preferring to lay out their workings by stakes at the surface. Early surveyors were often the early geologists too – they were the first to really appreciate the relationships between different rock types and mineralization.

The open fissure of Dirtlow Rake near Castleton and Bradwell. This was a major rake with deep mines below it. It is still being worked a short distance away but this section has been preserved. Pick marking of an old passage can be seen on the left wall. It has probably been reworked from the surface for fluorspar early in the twentieth century. (RB)

A large faulted rake at Putwell (Putty-Hill) Mine near Monsall Head, showing the horizontal grooves caused by rock movement. It was probably emptied of the former lead miners' waste calcite early in the twentieth century. (RB)

A narrow working on Moss Rake, Bradwell. Here the remains of wooden stemples can be seen. Either the waste they held up has broken through them or, perhaps more likely, they formed a floor for a level passageway through old workings. (PD)

Stone stemples holding up waste in the High Tor Mine at Matlock Bath, with Roger Flindall as a scale. This level, driven around 1830, was used to transmit power via rods from a water wheel on the River Derwent to pumps in the mine, some 300 yards away. It was later used to act as a pump way for one of the Peak's last lead mines, Riber Mine, of which the steel pipe can be seen on the right. The mine failed in 1959, largely since it had not been appreciated how effectively the 'old man' could work below river level using pumping. (LW)

A pipe vein, Blende Vein, in Magpie Sough, Sheldon. The layers of mineral lining the former solution passage walls are mainly calcite with a little zinc sulphide ore – blende. At the time it was found the cost of driving the sough had left shareholders at a low ebb. The announcement that some 40,000 tons of blende were available revived hopes and allowed driving to continue, though only some forty tons were actually mined. (RB)

Masson Cavern, now a show mine at Matlock Bath, is a huge pipe cavity, once lined with calcite, fluorite and lead ore, and was probably discovered in 1697 or earlier. It is likely that much of the mineral lining had collapsed and was found on the floor, needing little more than a pick and shovel to work it. (RB)

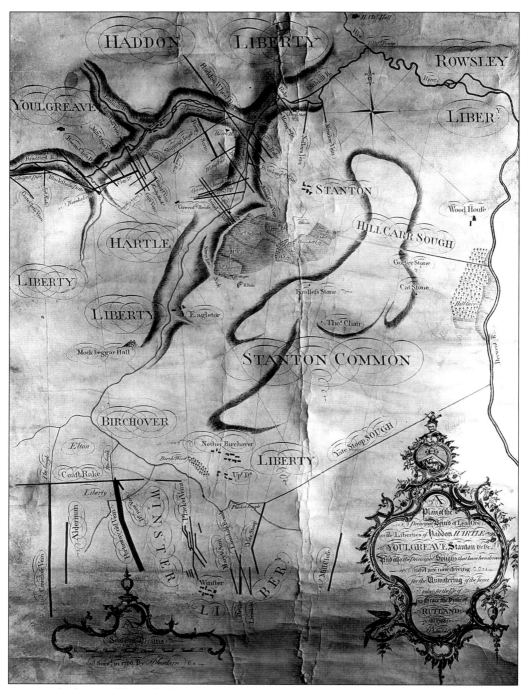

Maps and plans yield much detail on the extensive nature of many underground workings. This plan by John Nuttall is one of a series depicting the progress of Hillcarr Sough in the 1760s, showing not only the complex of veins at Alport it was intended to drain, but also those at Winster which were by then drained by the Yatestoop Sough, shown extending westward. (LW)

40

Five

Mechanical Power
in Mines

Water was the miners' chief enemy. Though it was possible to work in air so bad that a candle had to be left some yards behind them, miners could not work in more than a few feet of water. The construction of soughs was possible but enormously expensive so was avoided if possible. In any case, by the eighteenth century many mines were down at river levels and, in a few cases, below them.

If there was not much inflow, water could be bailed out, hand pumped, by churn pumps or by rag and chain pumps, or raised in barrels using a horse gin. Larger quantities needed some form of mechanical power – water or steam.

Water power was used occasionally before 1700, but generally water and steam power developed together, partly since the pumping system was a shared technology. Steam power was introduced to mining around 1710 by Newcomen, whose fire or atmospheric engine was probably first adopted on a mine in Cornwall. It then became fairly common on coal mines, where its prodigious appetite for coal could easily be sustained. In the Peak District, the first (and probably the first three) fire engines were adopted from 1717 onwards on Yatestoop Mine at Winster and were followed by many more, even being erected as late as 1824 at Magpie.

The much improved engine of Boulton and Watt was, however, also quickly introduced. Gregory Mine at Ashover installed one around 1785 and a few years later the first steam winding engine was also erected there. Steam winding was, however, slower to be adopted, but by the 1820s was becoming common and after 1850, predominant. After 1825, pumping engines were nearly all of the Cornish type, in many cases built and (superin-) tended by Cornish engineers imported directly from Cornwall. The last ceased working around 1930 at Millclose Mine, Darley Dale, when it was replaced by electrical pumping.

Though a very few substantial water wheels were used in the nineteenth century, notably in Lathkilldale and at High Tor Mine, Matlock Bath, and a few were used underground, as in the Godbehere mine under Cromford Moor, a better solution was developed by Richard Trevithick, the Cornish mining engineer, around 1790. In effect, he reversed the new designs of pumps and turned them into pumping engines, using high heads of water pressure which descended down shafts to the engine and discharged via the soughs. They were very efficient and about seven were used around Alport in the first half of the century, one being moved to Winster and remaining in use until around 1855.

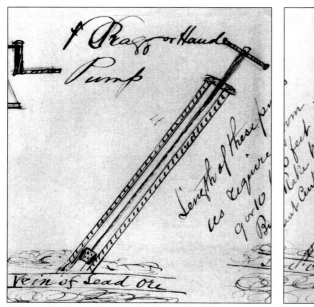
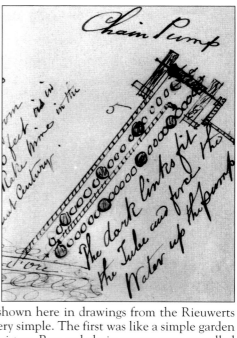

Churn (left) and rag and chain (right) pumps, as shown here in drawings from the Rieuwerts Collection at the Derbyshire Record Office, were very simple. The first was like a simple garden pump with a valve in the foot and another on the piston. Rag and chain pumps were so called because rags were used to fill the balls or pistons on a continuous chain which dragged water up a wooden pipe. 'Rolling the water' using 'rags' was some of the hardest work known to man, but with an output of about a thirtieth horsepower was fairly effective in small holes, though prodigiously expensive for deep mines which needed a series of lifts and many men. (DRO)

This photograph, taken in difficult conditions, shows a rag and chain pump *in situ* at Knotlow Mine near Monyash at the time of discovery, when water deep in the mine was being pumped out by modern explorers. (PD)

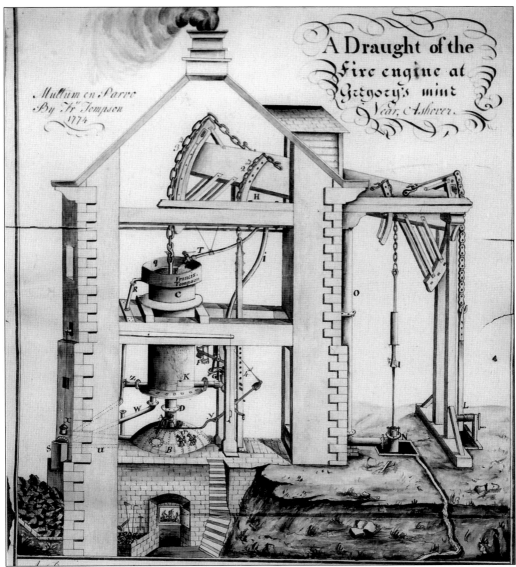

A drawing of a Newcomen Engine. This was installed at the Millclose Mine at Wensley c.1740 and was later moved and re-erected at the Gregory Mine, Ashover, by Francis Thompson, a noted engine builder whose business later moved to Chesterfield. (Ashover School, now in the DRO)

Hagg Mine at Matlock Bath in the 1770s used water power from the then rapidly flowing River Derwent. The water wheel was concealed behind the rocks on the far side and its power was transmitted into the mine via rods over the rustic bridge on the right. In the mine the change of motion was carried out by a bell-crank over the shaft. At this time there were probably four or five other similar arrangements in the Matlock gorge with wooden bridges transferring power over the river. The use of this declined, however, with the development of the cotton industry, which took over the best sites, depriving mining of their use. The original watercolour was by de Loutherberg. (Derbyshire County Council Collection at Buxton Museum)

Seeing underground pumps *in situ* is a rare event, but the very dry years of the mid-1990s saw the water level drop to the bottom of the pumps in Greensward Mine, near Monyash, and the opportunity was taken to record them. Here you can see the H piece of a plunger pump with the bolted covers that give access to the valves. On the right a wooden spar goes down to a lower pump which raises water to the cistern ready for pumping up to the next stage. (PD)

Left: This was the third water-pressure engine installed by Trevithick's men in Derbyshire and was made at Coalbrookdale in 1819. It was removed to Winster in the 1840s and placed in the Wills Founder shaft where it last worked around 1855. It used water from an earlier, high-level sough and discharged into the Yatestoop sough, here two miles from its tail on the River Derwent. Water is brought down the pipe and moves a piston in a cylinder, thus working the pumps, the top of which is 120ft lower than here which is already 360ft below the surface. The engine is now in the Peak District Mining Museum, Matlock Bath. (HMP)

Right: A view up the shaft showing the falling main down which the water flowed to power the engine. (HMP)

The mid-nineteenth century saw the development of much more compact, though lower powered, engines which did not require the huge houses and foundations of their predecessors. This engine at Bradwell was in the course of erection and used a boiler clearly developed from locomotive technology. (HMP)

This disused engine at Coalpithole Mine after 1880, on the other hand, used a traditional Cornish boiler, seen in front of the chimney. Most such engines were not only equipped to wind, but could also be geared to operate pumps and crushing machinery, enabling their economical use on quite small mines. (PD)

There are few survivors today of the engine houses that were built on many mines. Calver Sough Engine was erected soon after 1850 and moved to Magpie Mine in 1869. Its house survived for many years, opposite what is now the Eyre Arms at Calver Crossroads. (LW)

Meerbrook Sough engine house wound from a shaft sunk to the Meerbrook Sough when it reached Wirksworth around 1844. It had an unusual engine in which the cylinder swivelled to maintain alignment with the crank connecting rod, a type more usual in marine engines. The engine was within the near end of the house, the boiler at the far side. To the left of the picture is the mine coe, a low building with the floor lower than outside – once a type common locally though now this sole survivor is under threat. (LW)

This fine winding engine house and chimney at New Engine Mine on Eyam Edge wound from the Peak District's deepest shaft, over 1,000 feet deep. The chimney was needlessly demolished in the 1970s but the engine house has now been preserved. (RB)

Six

Dressing the Ores

When brought out of the mine, the ore, whether lead or copper, was usually mixed with earthy material and other minerals. Before it could be sold to a smelter it had to be concentrated by processes known as 'washing' or 'dressing'. The first need was therefore to sluice it with water to remove clayey stuff. Good material could then be picked out and put on the bing heap in the coe. Useless waste would go directly on to the hillock. Mixed material had to be broken down, using a bucking hammer, to a pea-size or below and was then riddled to produce 'peasy' ore which could be sieved or jigged and finer material which could be buddled. These activities were very much the province of the women, old men and children of the miners' families. It was hard work, often done under the sky on the high hills of the Peak, and generally shifts were much longer than for underground workers.

In the nineteenth century the washing processes gradually became more mechanised. The first change was the introduction of a horse-powered crusher to break the ore, and then a counter-balanced sieve needing much less effort to jig or 'hutch' the peasy ore. Both developments displaced women and by the mid- to late nineteenth century very few women indeed were employed. In the late nineteenth century at the few larger mines, the processes were further mechanised, with steam-powered crushers, sets of jigs and circular buddles that handled larger amounts faster and better than ever before. In the twentieth century ore became handled by belts and bucket lifts and different minerals – lead, zinc, barite and fluorspar – could be separated by a new process, flotation.

After dressing, the ore was sold. Except at very productive mines this was done at six- and seven-week intervals (i.e. eight times a year), when the Barmaster and usually two jurors attended the measuring, using the wooden dishes, removing the duties and permitting the remaining ore to be sold to ore buyers or lead merchants.

A woman washing ore at Gildereye Mine on the hillside above Matlock Bath, *c.*1770. She is plunging a sieve of peasy ore into a vat of water, which causes the lighter waste to rise to the top so it can be skimmed off. It is particularly heavy work. Her miner men-folk are represented, in a typical artist's ploy to avoid going underground, as favouring a distant prospect. (LW)

In a further scene painted by Day in the 1780s, men are seen sledging the larger pieces of ore, while a woman breaks it down further using a bucker and others appear to be sieving. The wooden trough is probably a standing buddle. In the valley are the buildings of the growing tourist spa of Matlock Bath, which had probably attracted the artist. (LW)

A vat or water tub used for washing ore underground in part of the Masson complex, Matlock. This was a common practice where there was sufficient space, since it avoided raising the waste to surface. Water was normally easily available and, at the expense of a few candles, the weather was always clement. (LW)

In a sloping buddle, a slurry of ore in water was poured down a slope so that the waste was washed further away. This buddle is on Bonsall Leys above the Via Gellia road. (LW)

51

The water was usually recovered for further use from a small pond at the end of the buddle, but in some cases was allowed to flow into larger slime ponds or dams to trap the poisonous slimy waste. These are the slime dams at Winster Pitts, dating from the 1860s. (LW)

From about 1820 horse-powered crushing, with an iron-rimmed stone running on an iron-plate circle, replaced the bucking hammer. This is outside the Odin Mine at Castleton. (RB)

The replacement for hand jigging was the hutch. This wooden hutch has survived because it was underground in the Old Jant workings at Matlock. Part of the axle and lever arrangement can be seen next to the box and John Pickin's reconstruction drawing shows how a larger sieve was counterbalanced, increasing output and decreasing the effort needed (RB).

This early twentieth-century concrete hutch, at Great Rake Mine on Carsington Pasture, was recognized by the bolts for the uprights, similar to those above (HMP).

The dressing floor at Ecton in the late 1880s. There was a steam engine in the 'house' and the ladder to the upper floor may also have been laid with rails to hoist waggons. The mine waggons were mounted high with an overhang to permit easy tipping. The open-fronted sheds would have had some form of crusher, jigs and picking tables and a circular buddle can be seen to the right. Scrap lying around and the general air of the lower picture suggest the remaining life of the site is short. (HMP)

Seven

Smelting the Ores

Most smelting sites were off the ore field, *en route* to the main markets and located near woods or coal mines for fuel and surface streams for water power. Once it had been washed to a concentrate, the ore was either packed in sacks and 'jagged' on packhorses or taken to the smelting works by horse and cart. Until around 1580 this was normally to a bole hill site on a high hill, particularly on the high gritstone edges running from east of Wirksworth to as far north as Sheffield. After around 1580 it was sent to the new smelting mills, which used water power to work the bellows for the blast. Usually these were sited in a valley close to a road and near sufficient woodland (often called a Hagg Wood because of this use) to provide dried wood chips or 'white coal' for fuel. Little remains of either of these kind of sites except for slag and the remains of water power channels.

From around 1735 the cupola-type smelting works developed using coal as fuel. A few new works were built, but since the older mills were usually close to coal, they were often adapted. These works have left some substantial remains, mainly in the form of condensing flues for the precipitation of particulates carried off from the surface. There are also several stumps of furnace chimneys while Stonedge, standing 65ft high on top of the moors above Chesterfield, is the oldest known free-standing industrial chimney in the world.

From the smelter, the lead pigs were usually sold to merchants in Chesterfield, Bawtry or Hull, who specialised in sending lead around the world. Before about 1780 this was frequently in the ships of the Dutch East India Company, but thereafter in English East India Company vessels. As a result, lead ingots or pigs have been recovered from many wreck sites around the world, a goodly proportion originating from the Peak.

Copper was a little different. In the eighteenth century it took some forty tons of coal to smelt one ton of copper. Coal was therefore taken by cart from Denby, near Ripley, to Ecton and a first smelting only used to separate the bulk of the waste from the dressed ore. The rich 'matte' which resulted was then carted back to Denby in the same carts and the remaining smelting processes done there. Other smelting sites were also set up nearer to Ecton, as at Whiston, using local coal. Little remains on these sites except for slag, but sometimes the molten slag was cast into blocks and used for walls, the black colour of which is very distinctive. At Denby many of the firebricks from a furnace there have been used to build garden walls nearby.

The lead-smelting house at Middleton Dale, near Stoney Middleton. The lower chimney belongs to the older smelting hearth which had used white coal (dried wood) as fuel. It had, by the time of this drawing, around 1815, been converted to a slag hearth for re-smelting slag. The higher chimney provides the draught for the coal-fired reverberatory, or cupola, furnace. Next to the building is a (probably Cundy's) limekiln, which would have supplied some lime for the smelting process, in which it was used to 'dry up' (solidify) molten slag so it could be drawn out of the furnace. The source is a pre-1818 coloured print by F.L. Chantrey. (LW)

A lead-smelting cupola on Cromford Moor, c.1815, from a watercolour in the Derbyshire Record Office belonging to the Derbyshire Archaeological Society. Near Black Rocks, this was almost on top of the important Gang and Godbehere veins – an apparently obvious site except that closure of these mines left it some way from other necessary resources and it closed a few years later.

A smelting cupola in the Via Gellia, in a print from J. Rawlinson's *Views of Derbyshire*, 1822. This is today a converted cotton mill site at the bottom of the Clatterway to Bonsall. Note how the chimneys in all three contemporary pictures are 'stepped' in a similar fashion, possibly since furnace building seems to have been dominated by a very limited number of specialists who were brought in as necessary. (Picture supplied by Doreen Buxton)

The only surviving chimney in the Peak District, at Stonedge Cupola near Chesterfield, before restoration around 1979. Robbed trenches on the site are from the network of flues that condensed the poisonous lead fumes. (HMP)

The flues at Meerbrook Cupola, on the road from Whatstandwell to Wirksworth, have several generations and extensions. The best sections have been buried to permit building development, including the arched section here, which divides a single flue into three parallel ones. This was the last section built and was scarcely used before closure around 1885. (HMP)

The final section, a long flue, leads to a (now destroyed) chimney on the hilltop. To enable it to be cleaned by brushing off the lead oxide dust and condensate (a job that would inevitably lead to lead poisoning) it has frequent roof entries and side doorways which were blocked while in use with stone and bricks. (HMP)

The remains of a condenser and flues at the Alport Cupola, *c*.1885. When built, after 1851, these were the most developed flues in the Peak District, with several parallel tunnels built around the hillside (beyond the left of the picture) before returning to a final condenser and chimney, seen in the woodland. The site is completely wooded today but the flues still largely survive. (LW)

Weighing ingots – here the very heavy 'great pigs' – from the Dutch East India ship *Kennermerland*, wrecked in 1664. The ship drove so hard into the voes, or inlet, of the Out Skerries in the Isles of Shetland that only the lookout was saved, being catapulted ashore from the crow's-nest. (Keith Muckleroy)

These small lead pigs were recovered in about 1975 from the *Hollandia*, a Dutch East India ship that was wrecked off the Isles of Scilly in 1743. They were probably taken via Hull and London to Amsterdam, and were on the ship's maiden voyage to Batavia, part of modern Indonesia. Some 240 ingots were recovered, many having Derbyshire characteristics such as shape, weights and marks. The photograph shows a sample back in Derbyshire. (HMP)

Marks on a lead ingot recovered from the 1698 wreck of the *Krajensteijn* off South Africa, the first ingots to be recovered from a Dutch East India wreck. Note the apparently much earlier date stamp. (H.E. Soonike, South Africa Cultural History Museum, Cape Town)

Eight

Mining for Vein Minerals from the Late Nineteenth Century

By the 1880s it had become clear that the traditional lead industry was dying. The growth of industry and transport inland and overseas, however, provided new opportunities and expanded older ones. Many mines began to be worked for what had often been regarded as waste, such as calcite, barite and fluorite and, in a few mines, zinc. Some iron and manganese oxides were also used, both for paint and for smelting to the metals.

The main new material mined was, and still is, fluorspar. This was available in enormous quantities on mine waste hillocks and was also easily accessible unworked or as stowed waste in many mines. It was worked by a large number of very small operators all over the area, with larger-scale operations especially on and under Eyam Edge, with the mill at Glebe Mine, Eyam, and, until recently, under Longstone Edge. Until the 1940s it was often possible to hand pick met(allurgical)-spar and until the 1980s, when higher grades were required, it was possible to treat it to achieve a saleable concentrate in a simple dressing plant.

From the 1960s there has been a marked concentration of production of fluorspar and barite production. The Eyam mill was replaced in 1965 by expansion at Laporte's new flotation plant at Cavendish Mill, Stoney Middleton, which still operated until 1999. Their feed came from the Dirtlow, Eyam Edge and Longstone Mines and from further away if amounts warranted. For instance, a large area of the Masson Hill workings was reworked in the late 1970s and 1980s by a vast opencast, operated for Laporte, which reportedly removed some 450,000 tons of fluorspar.

At Ryder Point, Hopton, another company, C.E. Giulini, based in Sardinia, occupied a former short-lived magnesium smelter building with an advanced fluorspar dressing plant, but the enterprise was later to merge with Laporte and the mill closed. The period of its working, the 1980s, saw fluorspar production come to a peak at some 250,000 ton of concentrate annually. Today this has declined to about 80,000 tons, despite new uses in chemicals and plastics.

Barite was worked in a similar way, but demand remained fairly low until the North Sea oil boom of the late 1970s and 1980s, which used the heavy mineral as a basis for drilling muds, used to control pressures in the drill hole. Much of the earlier demand had been satisfied by a few mines, such as the Golconda Mine near Brassington which was worked for many years until the 1960s by the Key family, mainly for colour and paint production. This was to be the site of a plant set up around 1980 to produce barite specifically for North Sea use, with ore tributed in from open working rather than underground mining. The plant failed to foresee both competition and level of demand and closed after a few years.

A mine on Carsington Pasture. The figures are Joseph and Joseph Repton, son and father, and (right) Samuel Bacon, in around 1880. The younger Repton, in a bowler hat and with an elegant walking stick, was apparently returning from the Barmoot Court. The mine probably worked barite and lead. It is possible that the large box is part of a set of jigs. (Original photograph owned by Barry Robbins of Pikelow Farm, Windy Arbor, Stoke on Trent. Supplied by Ron Slack)

Great Rake Mine, c.1900, with headstocks and a shed with either a steam engine or an early oil engine for the winder. The roof is of corrugated iron or steel sheet. The seven workmen have not been identified, but suggest the size of workforce. (Original owned by Miss Dicken of Brassington. Supplied by Ron Slack)

The Great Rake site today (this photograph was taken in 1981) still has the concrete bases of engines and washing equipment, one of the large winding wheels over the shaft and this crab winch. (HMP)

Longrake Lead and Calcite Mine also started working around 1885. This photograph from the1920s shows a wooden headstock and a steam winder house built of stone with a corrugated iron roof. (Nick Bromehead)

Longrake's main haulage level, supported by steel arches, was at 300 feet of depth and had loading chutes from the almost pure calcite stopes above. This photograph was taken soon after closure, with John Peel forming the scale next to a decline to lower levels. (PD)

Above and below: Magpie Mine was worked by the Garlick Family and others between the late 1880s and 1925. These two photographs show developments at the mine, the upper in around 1913 and the lower around 1924 after a new headstocks and boiler had been installed. The mine must have been pumped to the bottom in 1913, since John Puttrell recorded of the owner that, 'Mr Garlick came up (the ladders) from the bottom in 13 minutes!!!' This was on vertical ladders in stages between 30 and 100 feet long totalling 728 feet. Little was achieved in all these years. (Negatives supplied by the late Edgar Garlick, son of the owner)

Amongst the more indefatiguable miners was Eric Fisher of Winster, who died a few years ago. Denied a career where he began as the surveyor's lad at Millclose Mine (below) when it closed, he opened his own, at Portaway on the Elton-Winster boundary. This was one of the 'great mines' of the eighteenth century. Here, in the 1950s, is his new wooden headgear, replacing an earlier sinking tripod. (Eric Fisher Collection – HMP)

Eric Fisher is on the right, while Horace Woodhouse, another former Millclose miner, is in the chair. (Eric Fisher Collection – HMP)

Eric Fisher reopened two Portaway shafts, the first for H.J. Enthoven, the lead smelters from Darley Dale. He subsequently reopened what became known as Fisher's Portaway, seen here in 1958-1959. The young lad on the left is Eddie Fisher, his son, with Ross Webster of Bonsall, while Jim Slater and Eric Fisher himself are in the cage. (Eric Fisher Collection – HMP)

Underground, the workings were cavernous, developed just above a stratum of volcanic lava. Fisher hoped to work some thirty tons of fluorspar a day, but though this was often achieved, stoppages for one reason or another made it difficult with two or three men to keep up and it is unlikely the mine paid more than wages, if so much. (Eric Fisher Collection – HMP)

A father and son partnership, Guy and Louis Pearson of Bonsall, operated the High Loft Mine under Masson Hill, Matlock. A very small-scale mine, it was just over 100 feet deep and was worked using a pneumatic drill and explosive only where necessary, relying generally on a pick, a shovel and a wheelbarrow. Again in cavernous workings, the Pearsons wound ore in a small bucket using an oil engine. Their small concern lasted over forty years, ending in 1970. This photograph shows the winder and compressor houses soon after abandonment. (LW)

A large number of fluorspar mines operated opencast from the surface. This small crane on Whitelow, Bonsall Moor, worked the deep fissure of White Rake to depths of around 80ft. Men using pick and shovel filled a bucket holding about half a ton, which was swung into a three-ton lorry at surface. Somewhat larger ventures used a small dragline. (LW)

Jugholes on the western end of Masson Hill at Matlock used a winch-operated incline to haul out of the cavernous entrance. The waggons were then run down the hill to the loading point. (RB)

Miss Parkin's Mill at Ashover was housed in this rather nondescript asbestos-sheeted building. Miss Parkin was given £600 by her father to set her up in business around 1939. She chose fluorspar mining and milling, first reworking hillocks with men using barrows and hand sieves, then opening her own mine with herself as manager and shot-firer (overriding objections from the mines inspector) and, in around 1945, building this mill (LW).

The ore passed via a log washer into the mill. The log worked like an Archimedean screw, with a counter-current of water washing out clay and fines. (LW)

The cleaned gravel passed through screens and a crusher, seen on the left, and through the jigs on the right. (PD)

A bucket elevator was used to raise material from the crusher over the screens. (LW)

Modern underground mining: the occasion was the breakthrough from Laporte's Sallet Hole Mine to Watersaw Mine in November 1988. The two mines were then the chief underground producers for Cavendish Mill. Present are, from left to right: Nick Hardy (who is nowadays the manager of Laporte's Milldam Mine), Ted Fraser-Smith (mine manager), Alan Mackie, Charlie Knight, Brian Linley, Keith Valance, David Brown. (Laporte Minerals – HMP)

Laporte's Cavendish Mill at Stoney Middleton is the only major mill still at work in the Peak District. At its heart are the ball and rod mills, in which the cleaned ore is rotated in a drum with iron balls or bars and ground down to a fine flour-size. These were installed around 1965. (Photograph by Alan S. Marshall for Laporte Industries Ltd)

From the ball mill the pulp of water and ground ore is pumped through flotation cells which are agitated to produce a froth. The chemistry is adjusted so that specific minerals attach themselves to the bubbles, which spill from the cell into a trough where the bubbles are 'killed' with water. (Photograph by Alan S. Marshall for Laporte Industries Ltd)

The resultant slurry of water and mineral, which can be lead, zinc, fluorite or barite, is passed through vacuum filters to produce filter cake which is dried and packed ready for the market. (Photograph by Alan S. Marshall for Laporte Industries Ltd)

On surface mines the use of tracked shovels, notably the 'Drott', a 1960s conversion based on an agricultural tractor, and the ubiquitous JCB, replaced hand labour very rapidly indeed. Here at Tearsall Mines, Wensley, in 1974, a Frisch tracked shovel is loading into a 'beneficiator'. This is a loading device that rejects oversize lumps using a screen or 'grizzly'. Since the fluorspar is more friable than limestone, this gives a much higher-grade product for the mill. The JCB on the left awaits the next lorry. (LW)

The hydraulic back hoe, which became common in the 1970s, was another revolution in opencast mining technique. Here one is seen at work on Longstone Edge, loading into a dump truck. (Laporte – PDMM)

Nine

Millclose – The Last Major Lead Mine

Millclose began working in the early seventeenth century, one of a substantial number of lead mines in Wensley, and was drained by the Millclose Sough. 'Old Millclose', as it has become known by modern explorers, was taken over by the London Lead Company in the 1730s, but despite considerable expense and effort, including the installation of two steam engines and the driving of the deeper Yatestoop Sough, its water problems proved insuperable and work stopped in the 1770s.

Edward Wass restarted work on the mine in 1859, near its eastern and deeper end. A lead smelter, he unusually owned the whole mine himself. He put a Cornish steam engine on what became known as Watts Shaft and drove a level for a quarter mile south, to no profitable effect. Some ten years after he took the mine he then began to drive north, which had defeated the earlier company, almost immediately striking rich ore. Within a year or two it was clear the prospects lay still further north and he sank shafts at what became the 'modern' Millclose, placing a total of three Cornish pumping engines on them. The mine thereafter was generally profitable until the end of the First World War, being the most important producer in the area almost every year. After the war, however, it is clear that reserves were very low and that miners were doing little but 'picking the eyes' of the once great mine. Labour practices were extremely old fashioned and attempts to introduce, for instance, pneumatic drills, were nullified by the custom of only the team leader being allowed to operate them – one of whom was seventy-five years old! The mine was on the verge of closing and a final attempt was made, following a report by the famous mining engineer Malcolm McClaren, to sink deeper on the 'boil-up', a well of underground water on the 80-fathom (480ft) level which came up through a fault in barren volcanic strata.

This was successful, finding a vast cavern system at least 800 yards long with huge reserves of ore, enough to keep 800 men employed. McClaren had been employed by a new owner, Johannesburg Consolidated, to do the report and the international company introduced fully up-to-date methods. In 1937, however, a vast reservoir of water was tapped when the bottom level cut the Pilhough Fault. This flooded the mine, which took over six months to restore to full work. There was much further exploration but to no avail and in 1939 it was determined the mine was to close, with the last work, withdrawing equipment, done in 1940. Despite minor ventures since, notably the Riber Mine at Matlock and the Magpie Mine at Sheldon, this was the effective end of lead mining in the Peak, though lead ore remains a minor product of other vein mineral mining operations even now.

Watts Shaft with pumping and winding engine houses erected in 1859-1960. The men pictured include Edward Miller Wass, the owner (on the left in a top hat), who died in 1886. (PD)

Lees Shaft was sunk in the 1880s at what was then the furthest-north point of the mine. It functioned as the main haulage shaft. The figure on the left may be Daniel Morgan, the engineer. (LW)

Waggons coming up Lees shaft were pushed over the hopper on the right, which delivered into an endless-rope-hauled tramway to the dressing floors. (Stone Collection – LW)

This is the same tramway where it came above the dressing floors, close to the main part of the mine. The tall shear-legs are over the two shafts – Warren Carr (housing the Jumbo engine) on the left and Baby and Alice on the right – and were used for handling pumps and pumping rods in the shafts. (Stone Collection – LW)

Around 1912 an aerial 'flight' was constructed to bring in coal from half a mile away over the river, near the Darley Dale railway station. Other photographs show even longer ladders! The terminal station was attached to the Jumbo engine house. (HMP)

The large find of the 1930s led to complete rebuilding. Electric pumps replaced the steam pumps – this view sees the Jumbo engine house half demolished, prior to being later re-roofed – and these two enormous bins were erected to take ore from the two different royalties the mine was working. (Stone Collection – LW)

Underground, a new winder was constructed on No.1 Winze, well away from the main shafts, to wind from the 103-fathom level to the 70-fathom. (Stone Collection – LW)

The view at the bottom, on the 103-fathom level, changed but little, however. Here a waggon is being loaded into the cage just visible on the right. (Baker Mss. – LW)

The stows, or hand winch, was still used in what were known as 'wing deposits' – side veins off the 'main joint' of the mine. Frank Staton is on the left. (Foster Smith Collection – LW)

The ore from the working stopes was tipped down timber chutes, or shuttles, to run into the waggons on the 103-fathom level. (Baker Mss. – LW)

Lees Shaft was a favourite place for group photographs. Here in 1936 were, from left to right:
E. Needham of Darley, M. Hardy of Winster, Arthur Marshall of Winster, Frank Land of Bonsall,
Peter Boam of Winster, Jim Wood of Wensley, Bill Mosley of Winster, Cecil Newton of Winster,
Wilf Stevenson of Calton Lees and Joseph Varley of Darley. Note the safety lamps being carried.
These were necessary when working close to the shale. (Eric Fisher Collection – LW)

Another group photograph at much the same date. The notice warns against riding on the
waggons. (PD)

Processing the large amounts of ore led to new dressing methods being adopted. These circular buddles dated from the 1880s and probably survived until about 1930, treating the finer fractions of ore. (Stone Collection – LW)

In the 1930s finer fractions were treated on James or similar tables, which relied on a shaking motion to separate materials of different specific gravities. (Stone Collection – LW)

This view, probably *c.*1912, shows a new dressing shed being erected, with jigs and their functioning parts stacked outside. The bucket elevator took waste up to a high-level railway to allow disposal of tailings on the tips. (J. Marsden of Winster. Colln. LW)

A very similar view in 1923, showing various accretions and a much more battered appearance. On the left is the crusher house, with trommels in the centre and jigs on the right. The elevator can be seen on the far left and what appears to be an old boiler lies in front. (Francis Glossop, 1923 *Report*)

Here are the lads who worked on the dressing floor around 1936. From left to right, top row: Harry Bowmer of Holloway, Fred Flint of Wensley, Wilf Spencer of Bonsall, Dick Bond of Winster, Edward Stevenson of Rowsley. Middle row: Stan Marshall of Winster, Owen Smith of Bonsall, George Kenworthy (of no fixed abode!), Stanley Haynes of Cross Green, Charlie Stewartson of Matlock. Bottom row: Eric Fisher of Winster, Harry Goodwin of Birchover, Harold Boam of Winster. (Eric Fisher Collection – HMP)

Surface plant was again renewed in the 1930s. The most important dressing innovation was the flotation plant, which allowed both lead and zinc to be processed and separated. Most of the old dumps were reworked as a result, sometimes three times. (Stone Collection – LW)

Around 1935, at the peak of output, it was decided to build a new smelting plant adjacent to the mine. Taken a year later, this photograph shows the blast furnace for resmelting slag, with ingots of lead stacked in front. (Stone Collection – LW)

The lead smelter still survives today. Here, in 1951, pig moulds placed in a semi-circle are being filled from the furnace. Notice how small they are compared to lead pigs from previous centuries. (H.J. Enthoven Collection – LW)

The blast that sealed the mine's fate in 1937. Water poured in from the Pilhough Fault, drowning the lower levels of the mine. This much-battered photograph is from a German advertisement pointing out their prompt response with new power cables for the emergency. The initial inflow was very much higher. (PDMHS Collection – DRO.)

Appropriately grim-faced, the engineers and men who were about to go down to install the pumps (under the tarpaulin) after the flood. Pumping costs and failure to locate more reserves led to closure two years later. (Eric Fisher Collection – LW)

Ten

Quarrying for Gritstone

The Millstone Grit rocks have a wide range of sandstones, from very fine and consistent to coarse conglomerates. Within short distances of outcrops the rock has always been used for walling and building and for firestone, but its abrasive qualities led to the use for grinding, as whetstones and the eponymous millstones. The better, more consistent-quality beds can be sawn and tooled to produce fine ashlar for building and ornamental stonework.

Output grew rapidly as outside markets were opened by the development of canals and boomed with the advent of railways. The stone was especially favoured for large-scale projects, such as the Howden Dams in north Derbyshire, and in the fine houses of the Peak. After the Second World War, higher wages, the high labour input and a demand for mass-marketed alternative products (often, as it has turned out, of dubious merit) saw the closure of most of the gritstone quarries. Recently the demand has risen again, for building both within and outside the Peak Park, and several specialist quarries remain in production on Stanton Moor and at Grindleford.

Unlike rocks that are crushed for aggregate, dimension stone, as it is known today, had to be worked in large blocks, sometimes as much as fifty tons in weight. This meant that although simple hand-operated shear-legs and waggons on rails could be used, the labour input was very high and both gritstone and quarried limestone production was mechanised comparatively early. The huge, steam-powered, three-legged derrick became a normal feature of any substantial dimension stone quarry from the late nineteenth century onwards. Sawn stone, again either gritstone or limestone, was produced using either soft iron wire or frame saws with an abrasive, though nowadays the diamond-tipped circular saw has largely replaced these. For polishing stone (including black marble) water-powered machinery was developed by Henry Watson at Ashford, near Bakewell, as early as 1748.

Note
The term 'quarrying' implies the accurate cutting, or squaring, of the stone into manageable blocks for building. Unfortunately, the commercial use of the term has been extended to include rocks broken down to aggregate by blasting and crushing. Though this will offend the purists, the wider commercial use of the term is followed in this and succeeding sections.

Above and opposite: Stoke Hall Quarry at Grindleford started in the late nineteenth century and is still active today. These three scenes, probably of the 1920s, show the considerable pride the owners and their men had in their steam-powered machinery. Although it was quite possible, indeed normal, to handle blocks of stone weighing several tons with hand-operated 'three-legs' and small waggons on rails, the advantage of such steam-powered tackle is obvious. (Stoke Quarry Collection)

Among the best known quarrying companies nationally was the Stancliffe Stone Company of Darley Dale. Their quarry is shown here, high on the hillside with the typical three-legged derrick used for hoisting immense loads on to rail-served trucks that were then lowered down to the works. (Lewis Jackson Collection)

Here Stancliffe's typical product, millstones, used for crushing, grinding and pulping, await despatch. The hinged roof on the right was lowered in bad weather. (Lewis Jackson Collection)

Eleven
Large-Scale Limestone Working

Limestone also has a long history of use for walling and building, though less often in a dressed state than gritstone. Lime, produced from the stone by calcining in wood- or coal-fired kilns, was important for agricultural improvement and also essential for mortars and the more powerful cements. Until the canals and railways expanded, the markets, production and consumption were local and small-scale, farmers often having their own small quarry and kiln in a convenient bank. With canals and railways, however, large-scale industry developed rapidly. Lime burning grew particularly in areas such as Buxton and Peak Dale (where the industry is concentrated today), Wirksworth, Crich, Stoney Middleton and in the Hope Valley near Castleton (now a centre for cement production as limestone and the necessary clay rocks are found close by each other).

The unburnt stone in crushed and ground states also had very large-scale uses. George Stephenson developed the Crich and Ashover quarries for iron smelting in his Clay Cross blast furnaces and Stewarts and Lloyds had their huge Middle Peak Quarry at Wirksworth for the same purpose. The demand for limestone in railway ballast, in foundations and tarmacadam for roads, as aggregates for concretes, as ground limestone in agriculture, as fillers in plastics and for chemical production developed the huge demand seen today. Limestone now forms a huge industry dominated by large companies such as British Lime Industries (Tilcon), Tarmac and RMC.

Certain horizons (or strata) of limestone, because of their fine grain, encouraged use as a freestone or, because of their fossil content, have been used as ornamental stone, for such items as mantlepieces, statuary and large building projects such as, in the case of the Hoptonwood Stone, the Bank of England. Others, because of their purity, are especially valued by the chemical industry; the Middleton and Hopton limestone mines, worked from the Hoptonwood Firm's quarries, are now linked together underground, and are worked to result in such a high-purity product.

The earliest illustrations of lime burning come from Stoney Middleton Dale in the early nineteenth century. Coal was brought by cart from mines near Baslow and a load of lime was carted away in exchange, being sold to farmers on the acid soils between Baslow and Chesterfield. Chantrey's sketches of around 1815 show an already substantial local trade.

The Buxton and Wirksworth areas both benefited from the High Peak and Cromford canals, but the major growth developed with the linking railway, the Cromford and High Peak, which was in place by 1830 permitting easy import of coal and traversing the whole width of the limestone. The line used a sequence of levels, originally horse-drawn, and inclines, with waggons wound up and down by steam engines and chains. This photograph shows the bottom of the Middleton incline, near the quarries of Middle Peak at Wirksworth, in around 1934. (Roy Paulson)

The Middle Peak Sidings in the early twentieth century, adjacent to the Middleton incline. The site is today occupied by a coalyard. The building on the right seems to be a wheelwright's and the two men near the cart are using – or resting – a crosscut saw. On the left is a workshop. (Tony Broome Collection)

At around the same date, men at Middle Peak pose for their photograph. The railway appears to have a gauge of about three feet. (Roy Paulson)

George Stephenson and his partners developed the coal and ironstone mines at Clay Cross during the development of the Midland Railway. The huge market for lime and limestone was supplied from the limestone outcrop at Crich, the stone being lowered by gravity using a brake drum at the top of the incline, as shown here. (Biwater Company)

The incline came down to this impressive set of kilns at Ambergate, adjacent to the railway, and is seen entering on the right. The kiln bank, built around 1850, is reputed to have been partially made from the old stone sleeper blocks of the High Peak Railway. The lower stone section is conventional, if on a massive scale. The high iron-cased kilns, which gave a much greater fuel efficiency, clearly followed blast-furnace practice and were a later addition to only a portion of the original range. (Biwater Company via Stuart Band)

The view from the rear of the Ambergate kilns shows the kilns, with coal and lime hoisted in the first rise (left) to the top of the masonry section and in the second, to a gangway on the top of the kilns (right). (Biwater Company via Stuart Band)

The top of the limekilns at Hindlow, Buxton, showing a jubilee waggon of limestone being hand tipped into the top of a kiln. Behind can be seen the hoist and the lattice safety gates. (Mark Tomlinson, RMC)

The Hoptonwood Stone Company was set up in around 1880 by Colonel Hubbersty of Wirksworth to exploit the pure Hopton Limestone beds that outcrop on the hill between Middleton and Hoptonwood. In 1905 the Killers' Quarry, named after its Wirksworth family owners, was united with Hoptonwood to form Hoptonwood Stone Firms, which survived until the 1950s as monumental limestone producers and masons. Under the later ownership of Derbyshire Stone and Tarmac, the hill was transformed into a huge limestone mine. In this photograph, used in Hoptonwood's advertising in 1947, a workman ponders his next step. (Derbyshire County Council Local Collection and OMYA UK)

This photograph of around 1910, probably at Hoptonwood, shows production of stone blocks and aggregate. Hoptonwood used a narrow gauge (2ft) railway and small side-tipping waggons like these, with the wheelbarrow probably used with the plank to load from short distances away. (Tony Broome Collection)

The Stone Firm's monumental stone production was concentrated at the Middleton or Killer's Quarry, where, it was claimed, explosives were not used, the stone blocks being wedged out. Dominating the ornamental stone end of the quarry was the 85ft jib of the derrick. The removal of the upper beds produced much broken stone which was sent down to the quarry floor by a chute, loading into waggons of standard gauge. (Tony Broome Collection)

Above and below: Men at Hoptonwood pose for their photographs (no date but perhaps 1930s?). Note the hammers, which weighed about 10lb, though hammers as heavy as 28lb were used in local quarries. About eight tons per man would be broken and loaded each day. (LW)

Blocks of stone were taken over the road to the sawmill where they were cut using wire saws. The round-roofed building still stands at the time of writing. The works was served by the Killer's Branch of the Cromford and High Peak railway, a train arriving daily at a quarter to twelve precisely – 'you could set your watch by it', says Don Harris, who worked there. The stacked stones outside are gravestones for overseas war cemeteries which were the company's mainstay from around 1920 to 1930, when they produced and engraved some 350-500 a week. (Photograph W.M. Statham of Matlock, 1929, Tony Broome Collection)

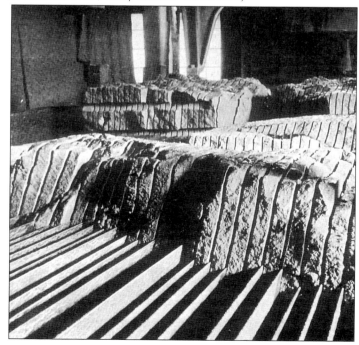

Frame saws in the mill cutting the large blocks of stone into slabs, probably c.1946. (Derbyshire County Library Local Collection and OMYA)

Killer's or Middleton Quarry in 1969. The new crushing and loading plant in a wholly lorry-served quarry. (Tony Broome Collection)

Over the hill at Hoptonwood, the quarry has a huge pile of blasted stone at the far end. This probably showed a transition from dimension stone production to aggregates, possibly c.1910. (Tony Broome Collection)

Soon there was certainly a development of the production of aggregates and dust. Here, a quarry, probably the Top Hole, was opened out using narrow gauge rail (on old full-size sleepers) to load into standard gauge waggons. (Tony Broome Collection)

The date of this picture is unknown, though probably post-First World War. Top Hole Quarry has a loading plant with a bucket elevator, possibly with lorries becoming used for external transport. (Tony Broome Collection)

Dene Quarry, begun in 1947, also works the Hopton Beds and began by extracting blocks for sawing and broken stone as aggregate. Here, the quarry with its derrick had only recently been started. Note the use of the railway with the almost ubiquitous jubilee waggons. (Don Harris Collection)

The base of the derrick and some of the extracted blocks, here being trimmed by pneumatic drill and plug-and-feathering. Left to right: Fred Spencer, ? Booth, Don Harris, Ted Squires, Herbert Hardy (then the owner), Derek Rice. (Don Harris Collection)

As the quarry grew, the face was served by a fan of railway tracks. Smaller blocks were broken by hammering and hand-loaded into the waggons. Present are, from left to right, front: Derek Rice, Don Harris, Bill Needham, Billy Gill, Archie Horseman, Les Statham, Jack Derbyshire and a representative of Hardy's Picks of Sheffield. Back: Bill Prince, Bill Spencer, 'Uncle' Spencer, Jeff Cobb, Dennis Hodgekinson. (Photograph Mr Hardy of Hardy's Picks – no relation to the owner. Don Harris Collection)

The work of loading broken rock was eased by the use of skips that could be hoisted off the heap or ledges using the derrick. This looks to be the entire workforce of the quarry at that time. Left to right: Jim Wood, Don Harris, Norman Henstock (the book-keeper), Herbert Hardy, Derek Rice (brother-in-law to Herbert Hardy), -?-, ? Spencer, -?-, Bill Doxey, 'Young' Fred Spencer. (Don Harris Collection)

By the 1950s, two types of stone were worked. The lower, sold as 'Hadene', came in both dark and light varieties and was creamy-fawn and fine-grained with various fossil skeletons, while the upper, sold as 'Derbydene' took a very high polish. Among major users were the Royal Festival Hall in London. The two horizons are easily seen here. (Don Harris Collection)

The cut blocks were transported to a sawmill beside the long-disused Cromford Canal and the Midland Railway. A travelling derrick was used for stacking the blocks and moving them to the mill. Don Harris used to set up the blocks for sawing in the afternoons, sometimes driving the travelling derrick. The sawmill still operates, though not, at present, using local stone. (Don Harris Collection)

This 1937 group photograph of workers in Cawdor Quarry at Matlock shows that quarrying methods for aggregate were much the same there too. (Tarmac Collection, Derbyshire County Library Local Collection)

In Matlock the face of modern quarrying began to emerge during and after the Second World War. Here, at Smarts Quarry in 1944, the bucket of a steam shovel seems to be loading into the old hand filling skips, which in turn were tipped via the small, travelling steam crane into waggons. (Tarmac Collection, Derbyshire County Council Local Collection)

At Cawdor the lorry revolution had begun by 1946, though rather delicately, as the picture shows. Fred Gill, later the quarry manager (left) and Alf Bunting can be seen prudently out of the way beyond the jib. (Tarmac Collection, Derbyshire County Council Local Collection)

By 1952, when the local quarries linked to form Derbyshire Stone Ltd, the Cawdor quarry was abandoning the old jubilee waggon and rail network and a new lorry-served plant was built. (Tarmac Collection, Derbyshire County Council Local Collection)

The 1950s saw purpose-built lorries for in-quarry use (seen here in 1955). They were able to convey as much as thirty tons to the crusher. (Tarmac Collection, Derbyshire County Council Local Collection)

Plant size grew rapidly. Here is the Buchanan primary crusher, the 'nutcracker', at Cawdor Quarry with its attendant, Fred Williams. (Tarmac Collection, Derbyshire County Council Local Collection).

The crushed rock was passed through rotary screens (above) and, inside the plant, conveyed by belts (below) to the appropriate hoppers for loading, usually (by the late 1950s) into lorries. Harry Crowder, the plant foreman, is seen checking all is in order. (Tarmac Collection, Derbyshire County Council Local Collection)

Twelve

Ornamental and Industrial Rocks and Minerals

The great houses of the Peak and the developing tourist industry that began just before 1700 provided a considerable local market for speciality stones and minerals , often mined underground. The first of these in importance and date was probably black marble, a muddy limestone which takes a fine polish. This was found especially near Ashford-in-the-Water. Here, by about 1748-1749, it was being mined by Henry Watson and sawn and polished by patent water-powered machinery. The stone was much favoured by successive Dukes of Devonshire, on whose estates the whole enterprise lay. The ornaments produced by Watson and many other craftsmen in Ashford are now very valuable indeed, and include some of the first-ever published geological sections – examples can be seen in the Buxton Museum and the Peak District Mining Museum. Associated with black marble was a range of other polishable limestones, including a red marble and various fine-grain and textured marbles such as those found in the crinoidal beds at Ricklow in Lathkilldale.

Blue John also began to be produced in the eighteenth century, supposedly discovered by the Hall family of Castleton. This is a yellow, blue and white banded fluorspar, found on Treak Cliff at Castleton, which has been turned in small workshops to make ornaments, personal trinkets and items such as bowls and vases. Even then it was estimated that only twenty years supply was left, much the same as estimated reserves today! Oakstone, a brown-banded variety of barite found near Arbor Low at Youlgreave, has also been used for ornaments but, though probably rarer, these do not seem to have the same appeal and antiquarian and auction room value.

Chert is a siliceous rock and is of common occurence within the limestone, usually as nodules. At Bakewell, however, great beds were exploited for the Stoke-on-Trent pottery industry. The chert was used for runners and pavors in mills and the roasted, or calcined, crushed stone, in the clay used for chinaware by Wedgwood and other manufacturers.

Around Friden and Brassington, solution of the limestone below a cover of Permo-Triassic sandstone rocks (otherwise entirely removed by weathering) led to subsidences in which naturally sorted sands and clays are found. These allowed the development of refractory brick firms located near the pits and the Cromford and High Peak Railway.

Of all these, today only Blue John is still mined, at the Treak Cliff Cavern at Castleton, though on a negligible scale. The surviving refractory brick plants now largely use imported materials and are wholly road based.

A nineteenth-century view inside the black marble mines at Ashford-in-the-Water. A similar photograph could be produced of the mines as they are today. (Derbyshire County Council Local Collection)

The Derby marble and stone works of Messrs Joseph and Thomas Hall, descendants of the discoverers of Blue John. (From *Commercial Aspects of Derby*, c.1860, courtesy of Roger Shelley, Derby Industrial Museum)

A chert bed in Holme Bank Chert Mine, Bakewell. The bed was undercut back to a joint or weakness and supported on the stone packs. When all was ready, these were blasted out to bring the bed down. It was then cut up into manageable blocks and dragged out on a tramway to the surface. The mine closed around 1965. (PD)

The workmen at Holme Bank Chert Mine, 1932. (John Willmot)

A small, blacksmith-made drilling rig, used in the Bees Nest sandpits in the 1960s to explore the sands and clays filling solution hollows in the limestone. To form the hole, a petrol-engined winch hauled and dropped a heavy cylindrical bailer attached to the end of the cable. (LW)

The bailer cut into the soft sand and had a small flap to prevent sand running out. Though rough and ready, it both allowed sampling and helped determined the depth of the pit. (LW)

Thirteen
Roads and Settlements

Since all the mining villages of the Peak had non-mining functions, it is hard to describe specific characteristics. The most noticeable is often their size – they are much larger than agriculture alone could support and did not have other obvious employment. A typical non-mining village on the high limestone hills of Derbyshire would hardly be more than a hamlet. Many mining villages also have good evidence of an unusual former prosperity. There are large houses, some three-storeyed with space for servants. Several villages have evidence of rebuilding, such as new fronts hiding earlier buildings. There were often many public houses and alehouses, traces of which may remain in house names; a 'Miners Arms' and a 'Pig of Lead' are good indicators! Infilling of land in the growing village produced the common small 'gennels' or alleys. Winster had a market and a market hall while Wirksworth had its moot hall in which the Barmoot Jury met.

Because many miners rented or bought a piece of land, there is often an unusual degree of subdivision of the formerly open fields and wastes. There may be many small stone barns surviving or found as low ruins in modern fields. The best clue of all, however, for determining lead mining villages is the enormous amount of traces of former lead mining, sometimes even in the centre of the village but rarely far away in the surrounding fields.

A few quarrying settlements did develop. Of these, Peakdale and Harpur Hill near Buxton are perhaps the most obvious, with late nineteenth- and early twentieth-century industrial-style housing that has few of the vernacular qualities typical of the lead mining villages. Brick and stucco, rather than gritstone and limestone, are typical especially of the 1920s and 1930s.

Very few roads were specifically constructed for the lead industry, though a few were dominated enough by the trade to be known as Lead Lane (for example, near Stonedge Cupola, Ashover). An exception was the road between Ashover and the colliery at Swanwick, which brought coal for the Gregory Mine engines. The Roman road network almost certainly respected the lead mining area, and settlements developed their own networks of paths, sometimes paved, for the local mines.

On the moors several routes survive that must have carried little but lead. The roads converged on smelting mills, for instance in the Cordwell Valley, on the River Hipper above Chesterfield. The development of improved roads and canals and the Cromford and High Peak Railway all emphasised the importance of lead, stone and lime as prospective freight. This emphasis still adds weight to modern campaigns for the restoration of the former main railway line from Derby to Manchester in face of the supremacy of road transport.

The Portway, seen here at Winster where this section is known as Islington Lane. A beehive-capped shaft of a small mine can be seen in the field alongside. The Portway (a post-Roman name) is reflected in field names near Wirksworth, Carsington (Lutudarum), the Portaway Mine at Winster and Alport and continues north across the ore field until it reaches Navio, the Roman fort near Bradwell. (LW)

Winster is the best-preserved mining village in the Peak, vastly oversized for its location at 900 feet above sea level and facing north. The Market House, here shown rather dilapidated in 1895, was built *c*.1730, when Winster was booming. The market was described as 'so throng, you could walk on t'heads o'crowd'. On the left is the sign of the Angel, where the High Peak Barmoot Court held its meetings, one of the twenty-four pubs in the town in 1750. On the right is a butcher's, home to one of the dozens of small tradesmen who once served the village. There is now a small exhibition in the Market House. (LW)

Winster Hall was built, or rebuilt, around 1709-1710 by Francis Moore for his son on the occasion of his marriage. Moore was a lawyer and overseer of Winster Sough, much criticised for its tardy development in the late seventeenth century. Mining litigation would have been a substantial part of his income, along with land he owned in the parish and elsewhere. (HMP)

Rather meaner houses on The Bank, the owners of some combining farming with mining as an occupation. (Photograph by A. Marshall, c.1905 – LW)

This fine house at the south-east end of the Main Street has been refronted, using a thin gritstone facing and mouldings, probably in the mid-eighteenth century. This disguised the age of the building but the position of the kneelers at the gable ends gives the deception away. The rebuilding reflects the considerable wealth coming into the village at that time. (LW)

At the top of the village at Islington Green, which was once a small settlement adjacent to the common or waste, is the orehouse. It was used in the second half of the nineteenth century by the smelter Edward Miller Wass to store his ore purchases from Winster mines. There are chutes at the back. It has now been restored and accommodates a small display. (LW)

Thomas Roberts' Barn. He was the Duke of Devonshire's Barmaster following the removal of George Tissington around 1760. Tissington was dismissed for near-fraudulent practices over collection of lead duties in Portaway Mine, where both he and the Duke were shareholders. Roberts had been the Duke's head coachman. He came to live at Banktop in Winster as Barmaster for the High Peak (leased from the Duchy of Lancaster) and the Duke's own liberties and rented the Duke's allotment of the Common after it was enclosed in 1764, when this barn would have been built. (LW)

Painters Way Farm, Winster. It is difficult to understand why the building was located in this muddy valley bottom until it is appreciated that the great Yatestoop Mine was close by and probably built it as the counting house. (LW)

Hollow Farm at Alport, a few miles from Winster. This was the home of Richard Page, the engineer to the Alport Mines, who installed the hydraulic engines there. The shaft was close to the house. (HMP)

A guidepost on the moors above Baslow on an old track known as Smilters Way. This was the route from the mines around Eyam and Stoney Middleton to the lead smelters in the valleys leading down to the lead market town of Chesterfield. (LW)

Fourteen

Caring For Our Mining Heritage

The process of caring for the heritage developed with the desire of those outside the industry to see and experience mining and quarrying. Leisure use of the area's mines – tourism – began some three centuries ago and was well developed two centuries ago, though the popular day trips that dominate the area today had to await the railways and promoters of rail excursions such as Thomas Cook – who lived in south Derbyshire. Both Celia Ffienes in the 1690s and Daniel Defoe in the 1720s commented on the lead miners in some detail, and it was not long before it was possible to hire a guide to go down an old or working mine. Matlock Bath and Castleton (the 'caves' in both places have mining within them) in particular became centres for this. At Matlock Bath there were over a dozen old mines used as show-mines at different times, with some four still doing so. Old mines today are also important for 'adventure tourism', with dozens visited frequently and some hundreds occasionally by both organised parties and small, specialist caving groups.

At Castleton there was an additional attraction until recent years. In the huge mouth of the Peak Cavern – the 'Devil's Arse' as it was known in less delicate times – ropemaking was carried out, originally mainly for use in the local mines. The methods used have been carefully recorded and may be reintroduced.

The easiest way of recording was by sketchbook and camera and in days where mines and quarries were regarded by all as providers of useful materials and employment there was sufficient pride by both visitors and those in the industry to ensure a record of what they were doing. Today the pressures created by the availability of cars and the popularity of living in an 'unspoilt' rural environment mean some of this pride has been lost and the task of recording and preserving has become somewhat specialist.

With over sixty sites considered worthy of being ancient monuments and scores more of local interest, this caring for the remains is a major task. English Heritage, County and Peak Park archaeologists and voluntary bodies such as the Peak District Mines Historical Society and its Peak District Mining Museum are very actively involved in this. Often, work on shafts and mines gives a useful and, sometimes, exciting experience of what work must have been like in the past, the huge investments of money and labour which were, almost literally, poured into the ground, the canny skills employed by miners and the risks they took.

Our pictures here show some of the most notable of preservation tasks, but it should be noted that many hundreds of hours are spent by volunteers in much less spectacular ways which, cumulatively, are probably of much more importance.

These two fine fellows were almost certainly ex-miners and were portrayed by Cruikshank in the late eighteenth century in a series of drawings of the Castleton caves. (LW)

At High Tor, near Matlock and Matlock Bath, two of the most spectacular fissures intersect, known as Roman and Fern Caves. They are veins worked from surface and are partly open, partly covered, so it is (still) possible to go through without lights. The artist has nicely conveyed the 'corrugations' on both sides of the fault. (Derbyshire County Council Local Collection)

The Great Rutland Cavern at Matlock Bath. This was part of the former Nestus mine, which had been worked since the thirteenth century, into which a tunnel for visitors was driven about 1810. The chandelier allowed visitors to appreciate the great height of the cavern but a more spectacular view was obtained from setting off Bengal lights, though the resultant smoke meant this was an end-of-day event only. (LW)

Magpie Mine, field centre of the Peak District Mines Historical Society, has been the focus of an enormous amount of effort to preserve it for the future. Here, in 1975, the engine house, which had been on the point of tumbling down, is being consolidated. The occasion marked the coming of age of the Peak District Mines Historical Society, reorganized, in recognition of its growing responsibilities, into a society limited by guarantee. (HMP)

In 1966 a shaft near the Magpie Sough collapsed, allowing hundreds of tons of scree to pour in and block the sough. A little later, after heavy rain, the pent-up water burst out of the shaft, displacing thousands of tons of scree into the river. This scene shows volunteers starting work to clear the entrance. From left to right: Axel Chatburn, Geoff Holt, Pete Meers, John Matthews, -?-, Hazel Matthews. (HMP)

Seven years later, the moment when the sough flowed again. Three million gallons of water rushed out of the unblocked tail into the river. Seconds before, the water had been pouring from the mouth of the shaft in the foreground. As a nineteenth-century miner commented on just such an occasion, 'and not a single person killed'. (Ron Duggins)

A few weeks later, with the work nearly complete, a new entrance arch was fitted (Peter Challis acts as a scale in this photograph). Trees were planted and today the area is a leafy glade again. (HMP)

This nineteenth-century view of the entrance to the 'Devils Arse' shows the rope-spinning machinery which still exists there. (LW)

A photograph from the 1970s shows that the equipment was still usable. Here it is being demonstrated by the last ropemaker, the late Bert Marrison. His ashes are buried near his equipment. (HMP)

Open shafts are a major problem. Efforts have at first concentrated on making those near footpaths safe. Here an open, almost invisible shaft at Brightside Mine, Hassop, some 250ft deep, has had a headgear erected to allow safe access to the top. (HMP)

Concrete sleepers are placed and once again it is secure. (HMP)

Not everything can be kept. The headstock (left), on Jingler Mine near Crich, disappeared overnight without trace, just a day or two after it was photographed in 1979. The pumping engine house on Old Engine Mine, also at Crich, had to be pushed into its collapsed shaft for public safety a little later. (HMP)

Where possible, the best place for preservation is on site. However, many mines are too vulnerable for this, whether because of human access, collapse or flooding. The 1819 Wills Founder engine was a case in point. With its drainage sough near collapse, it was dismantled in a sixteen-days-and-nights volunteer operation. Two years later it was well on the way to becoming the centrepiece of the Peak District Mining Museum where it can be seen today. (HMP)

After more than 700 years of continuous working, underground mining has now ceased in the Peak. As this book goes to press it has been announced that the last surviving enterprise, Laporte's Milldam Mine, and the associated Cavendish Mill are to close on 10 September 1999. The spirit of mining never fades, however. This is George Gregory of Winster, an ex Millclose miner, in 1976, aged seventy-one. Having watched the recovery operation for the Wills Founder engine for a week he asked to go down and, in a break in activity, did so. When called back up, the reply came: 'he's down t'sough.' (HMP)

Acknowledgements

The basis for this collection of photographs has been built up by the two authors over some forty years. These images are indicated by the initials LW and HMP at the end of each commentary. Some others derive from the associated collections at the Peak District Mining Museum (PDMM). The book includes many photographs that have been supplied to us by persons now occasionally forgotten. Though we have tried to give the original source, we apologise for any omission. The choice of photographs has been particularly strengthened by the work of two very active professional photographers who have permitted the inclusion of many of their prints, taken over a period as long as our own. We are thus especially grateful to Richard Bird (RB) and Paul Deakin (PD).

We have also been enabled to draw on photographs in libraries and in company archives or, sometimes, on company office walls, for which we are most grateful. This has included the Derby Industrial Museum, the Derbyshire County Council Library Local Collection at County Hall, Matlock, and the Derbyshire County Council Museum at Buxton and we wish to thank particularly Roger Shelley, Ruth Gordon and Ros Westwood respectively for their assistance. Many of the Millclose Mine photographs are now in the Derbyshire Record Office (DRO) at Matlock and we are grateful for the help and assistance the archivists there have given over many years and to those who have donated to their collections. The Revd Dr R.W.D. Fenn, the archivist for Tarmac at Wolverhampton, Mr Jeremy Hewitt of Omya UK at Matlock, Mr Rex Mellors at Biwater Co., Clay Cross, Mr Steve Hill at Buxton Limestone Industries (Tilcon) at Tunstead, Buxton, Mr David Jones and Mr Mark Tomlinson at RMC's Hindlow Quarry, Buxton, Mr Don Harris of Cromford, Laporte Minerals at Stoney Middleton and Philip Haywood of Stoke Hall Quarry, Grindleford, have all been extremely helpful and encouraging in facilitating and granting permission for the use of photographs in their care.

Most others who have given help and consent are colleagues at Peak District Mining Museum or fellow members of Peak District Mines Historical Society. These include Don Harris, Jim Rieuwerts, Trevor Ford, John Pickin, Stuart Band, Roy Paulson, John Willmot, Ron Slack, John Pickin, Bill Sargeant, the late Mike Smith and the first author's wife and daughter, Sheelagh Willies and Clare Henderson-Howat respectively. Many of the photographs would certainly have been impossible without the assistance and work of PDMHS members and, though it is not possible to mention all by name, we hope they still think it was worthwhile. Of non-members, but friends with similar interests, Doreen Buxton, Tony Broome and Ron Duggins, all of Matlock, and Lewis Jackson of Darley Dale have been as generous as always. Lead ingot pictures were taken by the late Keith Muckleroy and H.E. Soonike of the South Africa Cultural Museum at Cape Town and the photograph of the antler tool was by Graham Bunting. Other photographs have been provided by Mrs Dickens of Brassington, J. Marsden and the late Eric Fisher of Winster and Barry Robbins of Stoke-on-Trent. Three negatives of Magpie Mine were kindly supplied to me many years ago by the late Mr Garlick, son of the former mine proprietor, and the late Mike Smith provided the negative of the Nuttall plan.

We are grateful, too, to Sheelagh Willies for the careful proof-reading and correction of minor errors – those remaining belong to us. Finally, we have been much encouraged by our editor, Tom Cairns of Tempus, whose gentle queries have meant the completion of the work was not too late.

Thank you all.
Lynn Willies, Harry Parker.